THE LISTENER

For Barny, George, Polly, Sally and Fred

This edition published 2010
First published 1997 by
A & C Black Publishers Ltd
36 Soho Square, London, W1D 3QY

www.acblack.com

ISBN 978-1-4081-2235-8

A CIP catalogue for this book is available
from the British Library.

This book is produced using paper that is made from wood
grown in managed, sustainable forests. It is natural, renewable and
recyclable. The logging and manufacturing processes conform to
the environmental regulations of the country of origin.

Printed and bound in China by C&C Offset Printing.

THE LISTENER

Elizabeth Laird

Illustrated by Pauline Hazelwood

A & C Black • London

CHAPTER ONE

It was Friday afternoon and school was over for another week. Gavin Foster should have been in a great mood.

But he wasn't. He was depressed. He was fed up. And he was furious with his mum.

Just because you're going away for the weekend, I don't see why I've got to go away, too. I could have stayed here on my own, easily, or gone to one of my mates.

6

Gavin walked down to the bus stop. A crowd of his friends was standing outside the fish and chip shop.

The bus came. Gavin climbed on board and sat hunched at the back, hardly bothering to look out of the window.

He knew the road up to old Mrs Foster's cottage well. He'd often stayed there, ever since he was a little kid. He liked it up on the moors, as a matter of fact, and he wouldn't have minded spending a weekend there with his gran, if it hadn't been for the football match.

Johnny Mason's debut! His first game with Sunley United since his million pound transfer, and I'm going to miss it!

It had begun to rain. The old red-brick houses and narrow streets of Sunley looked dingy and depressing in the dull light. The bus wound its way out of town and had soon left the last house behind. As it climbed higher, up towards the moors, the rain turned to sleet and then to thick, driving snow.

The bus turned the last sharp corner before the top of the hill. Gavin picked up his bag and pushed his way to the front.

CHAPTER TWO

The biting wind, laden with snow, stung his cheeks. Gavin zipped
up his jacket and began to trudge down the path that led across
the open moor towards Mrs Foster's lonely cottage. He shivered,
and started to walk faster. He could see a light in the window
now and he knew his gran would have cooked a great
supper for him.

Gavin was nearly at the cottage door when he almost tripped over something. He looked down.

The telephone wire's collapsed! The weight of the snow must have brought it down.

Bad luck, Mum! I won't be able to phone you after all.

He knocked on the front door, but Mrs Foster didn't open it at once, like she usually did.

Gran! Are you there?

No one answered.

Gavin waited for a moment. He couldn't hear a sound.

Maybe she can't hear me.

He tried the door. It wasn't locked, so he opened it and went inside. The room was empty.

Gran! Where are you? It's me, Gavin.

No one was there, not even Tinker, the cat.

15

Gavin looked around the warm, cosy little room. The table was set for two people and he could smell a delicious smell coming from the tiny kitchen. One of Gran's casseroles was cooking in the oven.

Suddenly, he ducked in terror as a black and white streak
shot past his head.

Mrs Foster's tame magpie settled on the table and strutted
up and down, looking nervously at Gavin. The kerfuffle had
disturbed something else, too. A rustling, scrabbling noise came
from a box near the fire.

Gavin went over to look. Two small black eyes peered up at him from inside a halo of prickles.

A hedgehog! Trust Gran!

But where is she? And where's Tinker?

He ran upstairs and
looked quickly into the
two tiny bedrooms.

Are you there,
Gran?

Nobody answered.

He went to the front door and stepped out again,
into the driving wind.

She must be outside
somewhere.

And then he saw them. Footsteps were printed in the snow, leading away from the cottage, along the bend of the hillside towards the woods.

Something must have happened. She wouldn't go out for nothing on a night like this. I'd better go and look for her.

It had stopped snowing and the clouds were beginning to clear away but the daylight was going fast now and the snow-covered moors looked strange and eerie. Gavin kept his head down, his eyes on the footprints.

Suddenly, he stopped. He had reached a spot where the snow was trampled and messed up, as if there'd been some kind of struggle.

What could have happened? What a mess!

It looks like there's been a fight.

Leading away from the beaten snow were several sets of prints –
the ones he'd been following already, some tiny paw marks that
could have been a cat's, and some larger prints, like those of a dog
or a fox. And in the snow, bright as poppy petals, were drops of
brilliant scarlet. Gavin knelt down to look at them.

CHAPTER THREE

Gavin looked round. The human footprints went on towards the wood, but they had changed. They were more spaced out now, as though the person had been running. The moors Gavin thought he knew so well looked suddenly menacing in the fading light.

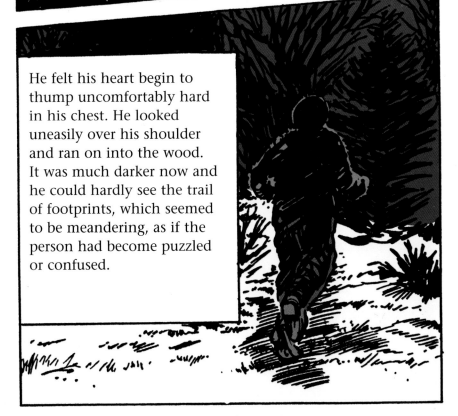

He felt his heart begin to thump uncomfortably hard in his chest. He looked uneasily over his shoulder and ran on into the wood. It was much darker now and he could hardly see the trail of footprints, which seemed to be meandering, as if the person had become puzzled or confused.

Twigs seemed to reach out and touch him and shivers of fear ran down his spine. All of a sudden he trod on a rotten branch which was lying just under the snow. It broke with a loud crack. Gavin nearly jumped out of his skin, but he steadied himself and went on.

Then he heard a noise. He stopped to listen. There it was again. Someone was groaning! His skin prickled with fright as he tiptoed cautiously towards the noise.

Then he saw it, a long dark shape under the trees. Someone was lying in the snow.

Gran!

Gavin ran up and sank down onto his knees beside the still figure. Even in the darkness he recognised her.

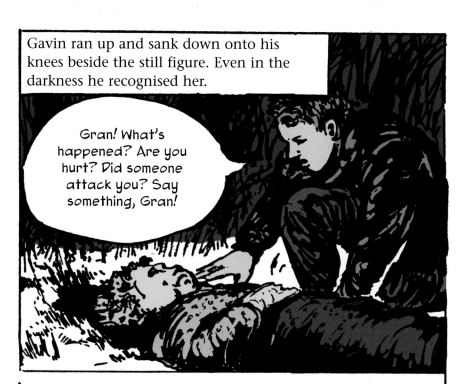

Gran! What's happened? Are you hurt? Did someone attack you? Say something, Gran!

The old woman opened her eyes.

Gavin! Oh, thank goodness you've come. It's my leg. I think ... I'm sure it's broken.

Gavin bent down and tried to lift her shoulders.

Hang on to me, Gran. I'll help you up and get you home.

No! I can't move. You'll have to go for help. My telephone's out of order but there are new people in the cottage just beyond the wood. I heard their car earlier. I'm sure they're there. Go and ask them to ring for an ambulance.

Gavin tore off his jacket and tucked it round her, then he took off as fast as he could through the trees.

He knew the cottage. It had been empty when he'd been here as a little kid and he'd often played round it. He hadn't realised that new people had moved in.

The cottage was much grander than he remembered. An extension had been built on one side and there was a fence all round it. Gavin opened the gate and went up to the front door. He rang the bell.

CHAPTER FOUR

The door opened at once. A woman stood there. She was big, blonde and angry. Behind her, Gavin caught sight of a darker, young girl who was watching him with an intent expression on her face.

A man's voice called out from upstairs.

Who is it, Sharon?

Another of your precious fans. This one's made up some stupid story about an accident.

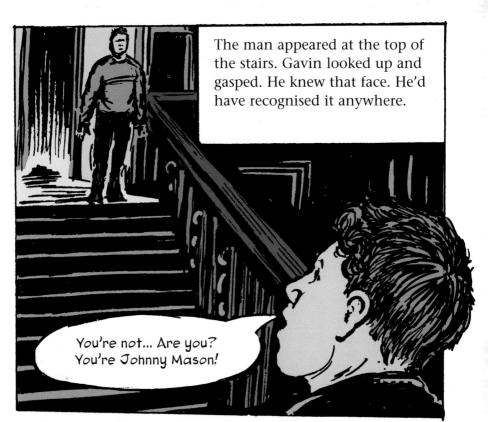

The man appeared at the top of the stairs. Gavin looked up and gasped. He knew that face. He'd have recognised it anywhere.

You're not... Are you? You're Johnny Mason!

I don't believe it! What have I got to do to get away from idiots like you? Buy an igloo at the North Pole? You're the fifth kid to bang on my door today!

34

Tears of helpless rage stung Gavin's cheeks.
He pounded furiously on the door.

Help! You've got to help me! My gran's in real trouble. She might die!

THUMP THUMP

A window opened above and a boot came flying out of it, nearly hitting Gavin on the head.

Leave us in peace or I'll call the police!

As the window slammed shut again, Gavin felt somebody tapping him on the shoulder. He turned round.

The dark girl he had glimpsed inside the house was standing behind him. She stood looking at him, a puzzled expression on her face.

Listen! You've got to listen! My gran's hurt. She'll die of cold if I don't get help soon.

The girl shook her head, then took hold of Gavin's arm and turned him round so that his face was lit by the beam of the lamp above the foot door.

What's the matter?

Her voice sounded as if it came from the back of her throat. Gavin could hardly understand her.

My gran. I told you. Are you deaf, or what?

She nodded vigorously.

Yes. Deaf. I'm deaf. Tell me again. I can read your lips.

He could feel the cold eating into him, sapping his strength. He was just about to give up hope and dash back to the woods when at last the girl returned.

Call the ambulance. Wait. I'm coming. Wait here.

She disappeared again, round the back of the house.

She rang off. Gavin looked up to see the girl hurrying back to him. Her arms were full of blankets and pillows and a torch was balanced on top of them.

CHAPTER FIVE

It was quite dark by now. The only light came from the unearthly white radiance of the snow. Out in the open, Gavin could follow the trail of his own footprints quite easily, but it was difficult once they were among the trees. He had to go slowly, peering down at the ground to find his way.

Suddenly, he realised he was lost.

But the girl had seen him stop and look around.

Use the torch!

With a shudder of relief, Gavin switched it on. There were his footprints, only a few metres away. He ran along them and there, a little further on, he saw the long, dark shape of his grandmother. She was lying horribly still in the snow.

Gran!

Gavin raced up to her, his stomach tight with fear. Was she still alive? Had the cold been too much for her?

He dropped down beside the old woman and shook her gently by the shoulder. Her eyes fluttered open.

So cold...

The girl knelt down beside Gavin. Gently, she lifted the old woman's head and Gavin, seeing what she was doing, took the pillow and tucked it into place. Then she began to wrap the blankets round his gran.

You're shivering. Put your jacket on again. She's got the blankets now.

Gavin lifted the jacket, which was still covering his gran's chest.
A black shape uncurled itself and streaked off across the snow
with a terrified yowl. Gavin and the girl started back with fright.

Tinker!

Don't let her run
away again...

Gavin laughed shakily.

Don't worry, Gran. We'll go after her in a minute. Let's get you comfortable first.

He wrapped the blankets round her, tucking them underneath as far as he dared, though she groaned with pain whenever he touched her leg.

Tea. I've got a cup of tea for you.

Gavin was getting used to the girl's way of speaking now. Although he missed some words, he could understand most of what she said, but Mrs Foster looked up at the girl, puzzled.

She's deaf.

That's why she speaks like that. You can talk to her, though. She's *good* at lip reading.

He kept his mouth away from the torch so that the girl wouldn't be able to lip read his words.

Mrs Foster murmured something. She spoke too quietly for Gavin to hear, but the girl seemed to understand what she wanted to say even though it was too dark for her to read the old woman's lips.

Who...

I'm Shelley. I'm Johnny Mason's sister.

Don't worry, Gran, we've phoned for help. They promised to send...

Listen! What's that?

He lifted his head. He had heard, in the distance, the roar of a helicopter engine. It was coming nearer. He could see its lights now, winking through the bare trees.

The air ambulance!

CHAPTER SIX

Shelley was holding Mrs Foster's hands, rubbing them between her own. She had heard nothing.

Gavin touched her arm and pointed to the lights above. Then he shone the torch onto his lips.

They're coming. It's the air ambulance. Stay here with Gran. I'll go and show them the way here.

Shelley nodded. Gavin took off like a hare, bounding through the wood towards the open moor. The helicopter was almost overhead when he ran out from under the trees. He jumped up and down, waving his arms like a madman.

The great machine slowly settled on the frozen moor, the wind from its propellers churning the snow up in a wild white storm. The door slid back and three people jumped out.

Over here! This way!

They pulled a stretcher and some bags of medical equipment out of the helicopter.

Don't go so fast, lad.

The oldest ambulance man panted as he followed Gavin into the wood.

Keep that torch still, will you? No point in all of us crashing into the trees and breaking our legs.

A few minutes later, they had reached Mrs Foster, and in what seemed like no time at all, she had been tucked on to the stretcher and the ambulance crew were gently sliding it into the helicopter.

The old lady had kept her eyes shut, wincing with pain whenever she moved, but just as the pilot was about to close the door, she opened them wide and looked at Gavin.

Promise you'll find Tinker and look after Gussie for me, and the hedgehog. And there are the ducks to feed, and...

Don't worry, Gran. They'll all be fine. I promise.

The crew climbed into the helicopter.

Gavin nodded, then the pilot shut the door, the helicopter's huge propellers began to whirl round and round, and the gleaming machine lifted itself effortlessly into the air.

CHAPTER SEVEN

Gavin stood for a long time, watching until the helicopter's lights had disappeared over the horizon towards the glow of light from the city below.

What do I do now?

He didn't like the idea of staying in Gran's cottage all on his own, but he had no choice. He looked round. Shelley had disappeared.

I suppose she's gone home. Back to Johnny Mason and that awful woman.

He thrust his hands deep into his pockets, hunched his shoulders and walked back towards the cottage.

As he pushed the door open, a smell of burnt food hit him right in the nose.

Oh no! The casserole!

Gavin ran into the kitchen, turned off the oven and pulled out the big dish inside it. The top of the stew was blackened, but underneath it looked fine. Appetizing, in fact.

Gavin suddenly realised he was hungry. He was still cold, too. He fetched a plate and fork and put them on the table.

At least I won't starve.

He was just about to help himself to some of the casserole when he heard a sound outside the front door.

No one answered.

The door opened. Shelley came in, and in her arms was a big black cat.

Tinker!

How did you find her?

I just called and she came.

Tinker struggled out of Shelley's arms and walked stiffly towards the fire. She lay down and began to lick at the dark blood that had congealed along her flank.

Gavin turned Shelley to look at him.

Is she badly hurt?

She bent over the cat and gently stroked the matted fur away from the ugly looking gash. Tinker snarled at her and pushed out her claws, but to Gavin's surprise she didn't try to scratch Shelley or leap away from her touch.

Not bad.
Best thing is to let her rest. She'll lick the wound clean. Give her something to eat.

67

69

CHAPTER EIGHT

A sudden loud knock on the door made Gavin jump.

Nervously, he opened the door.
Into the room stepped Johnny Mason.

Before Gavin could answer, Shelley flew past him and Gavin watched with amazement as she began flicking her hands and fingers about in a tirade of complicated gestures.

71

There was more frantic signing from Shelley.

Gavin shook his head in disbelief. Then he caught Johnny's eye. They both laughed.

Gavin put another plate on the table and began to dish out the casserole.